DON'T PANIC!
A HITCHHIKER'S GUIDE TO PANICKING

Caleb Nichols

ISBN: XXX-X-XXXXXX-XX-X

Cover designed by Aaron Kent

Edited by Cathleen Allyn Conway

Typeset by Aaron Kent and Cathleen Allyn Conway

Broken Sleep Books Ltd
Rhydwen
Talgarreg
Ceredigion
SA44 4HB

Broken Sleep Books Ltd
Fair View
St Georges Road
Cornwall
PL26 7YH

Also by CALEB NICHOLS

Books

Teems///\\\Recedes	(2021, Kelp Books)
22 Lunes	(2020, Unsolicited Press)

Music

Ramon	(2022, Kill Rock Stars)
Clarion	(2021, Kill Rock Stars)

Contents

Don't Panic!

Nichols

Words & Music

Playlist at bit.ly/panicsongs

1. It Is Happening Again // "Silver Soul" by Beach House
2. Ten Minutes // "10 Minutes 10 Years" by Tennis
3. How Does It Feel? // "Blue Monday" by New Order
4. Don't Panic // "Ladies and Gentlemen We Are Floating in Space" by Spiritualized
5. The Next Episode // "The Next Episode" by Dr. Dre & Snoop Dogg
6. Three Brains // "White Rabbit" by Jefferson Airplane
7. April Fools // "Idiot Heart" by Sunset Rubdown
8. Negative Capability // "I Want The World To Stop" by Belle & Sebastian
9. Breathing // "Breathe Deeper" by Tame Impala
10. Practicing // "The Practice of Love" by Jenny Hval featuring Vivian Wang
11. Feeling // "There, There" by Radiohead
12. Meditating // *"Twin Peaks* Theme" by Angelo Badalamenti
13. Connecting // "Connection" by Elastica b/w "Connected" by Stereo MC's
14. Moving // "Myself into It" by the Rapture
15. Fear-ing // "In Particular" by Blonde Redhead
16. Caring // "i" by Kendrick Lamar
17. Loving // "True Love Waits" by Radiohead
18. Being // "Little Person" by Jon Brion
19. Non-Being // "Float On" by Modest Mouse b/w "Flow" by Laurie Anderson

Author's note

This book is not cannot and should not constitute medical advice or the advice of a licensed mental health professional. My hope, as its author, is that this slim tome points you or a loved one suffering from panic episodes, anxiety, or other mental health disturbances, towards the care of a qualified mental health professional.

1. It Is Happening Again

Oh no, oh no, oh no.

That's the first thought when it starts: suddenly there, out of the blue. A presence at once menacingly unknown and sickeningly familiar. Panic number one hundred and seven. Or two. Or fifteen.

It doesn't matter the number, just that it's happening again.

2. Ten Minutes

Ten minutes.

That's how long it's going to last. At least the really bad part. The part where—even though you've been through this, or have read about it before—you aren't exactly sure what's happening. *Maybe this is something different,* the panic unhelpfully suggests.

It isn't. You are having a panic episode. It is going to last for ten minutes, and then it's going to start getting better by degrees. Here's a list of things you can do for 10 minutes:

> Wash the dishes.
> Fold the laundry.
> Organize a cupboard.
> Walk the dog.
> Listen to a few of your favorite songs.
> Take out the trash. And the recycling.
> Walk yourself around the block.
> Write.
> Read.
> Breathe.

I mean really you can do anything for 10 minutes if you think about it. The point is, at the end of ten minutes you are going to be two things:

1. Still alive, and
2. Feeling better.

And then 10 minutes after that, you're going to feel better still, and 10 minutes after that—a full thirty minutes after this panic tried to ruin your day—you are going to feel almost normal.

And although you were a bit beside yourself for a moment there, you'll realize that it's winding down, that the panic has left the building. Then, once you feel sure it's gone, you'll go back to feeling like you again.

And what a wonderful feeling that is, eh?

3. How Does it Feel?

How does it feel?

Symptoms caused by panicking include but are not limited to:

Rapid heartbeat
Heart palpitations
Skipped heartbeats
Dizziness
Chest pain
Having trouble breathing
Vertigo
Feeling suddenly cold
Tingling or numbness
An overwhelming feeling of doom
Sweating, cold or hot
Feeling out of body
Dissociating
Feeling like you're going to pass out
Feeling like you're losing control
Feeling like your head is on fire
Feeling a sudden heaviness
Feeling like something is wrong and you're going to die
Premonitions of catastrophe
Terror

The list could go on. If I've missed your most popular symptom, write it in the margin, or tweet them to me—I'm @seanickels.

Here's the good news: you can be experiencing any or all these symptoms and be having a panic attack instead of the big bad thing you—at this moment—think is happening. Panic is a sneaky little devil and a master of disguise; it likes to take you by surprise, dressed up as something else.

A heart attack. An aneurysm. A stroke. A brain tumor. Cancer. Spinal meningitis. MS. Schizophrenia. Parkinson's. A surreptitious and lethally venomous spider bite. An infection, beginning in that sore tooth you've had all week, that has suddenly spread—and if left untreated—will undoubtedly lead to sepsis and sudden death.

These are all costumes that panic likes to wear in order to do the thing it likes to do: scare the bejesus out of you, as my Granny used to say. I should mention that I've Googled the term symptoms of for each of the words on the above list, numerous times, and probably will do so again.

This is a bad idea.

I've found that Googling symptoms almost always fans the flames rather than puts them out. The algorithms that power these searches are trying to be helpful. They dutifully scour the internet for your search terms, which are invariably tied to one awful disease or another.

And then you have your algorithmic diagnosis:
Tumor. Not benign.

Also:

a pop-up asking you if you need help with your will.

It makes sense: panic disguises itself as other things, and so the internet thinks that your panic symptoms are heart attack symptoms, or something else.

When I feel I need to look up my symptoms, I turn to Calm Clinic's symptom list, just to remind myself that the random stabbing pain in my chest is still listed as a symptom of anxiety. It's a pretty exhaustive list, and it just helps me see this physician-compiled list of extreme ailments to remember: anxiety is a shape-shifting alien that *wants* me to think the worst. Here's that link: *https://www.calmclinic.com/category/anxiety-symptoms.*

Another strategy—for those with access, or indeed for whom this even applies—and my go-to in moments of extreme duress: call the nurse helpline on the back of your insurance card. You can tell them all the symptoms you are having, and they will give you good advice. Most likely they'll say, *well that sounds suspiciously like a panic attack.*

You can also call or text or chat with someone at a 24-hour hotline. They are staffed with volunteers, many of whom have been there (and back). The number for the American national crisis hotline is 988. It's staffed 24 hours a day, seven days a week. If you prefer to text, you can text HOME to 741741. In the UK you can dial 111 to speak with someone. And look, I know that sometimes these interactions are, erm, less than perfect (see chapter 8 for more on that) but it's quite a good thing to have somebody on the other end of the wire who might just listen.

It's a great idea to talk to someone, even if you are "just" dealing with anxiety: panic is a *real thing* that is a beast to go through alone, and bringing another human being into the equation—even if they are only on the other end of a call or a text—is often an effective way to break the hold panic tries to strangle you with.

So don't be alone. You don't have to be.

4. Don't Panic

Don't Panic!

What a terrible thing to say to someone who is panicking. Possibly it is the worst thing you could say as an onlooker, and the worst advice you could get as a panicker. It's the equivalent of yelling *don't be on fire!* to a burning building.

The building is already on fire and at a particular point it's probably best to just make sure everyone gets out safely, contain the flames, and let it burn itself out. And this is the thing with panic—once it's started, it's already too late to stop it.

The trick is twofold: to know that if it does happen, it's going to burn itself out (typically within 10 minutes) and to try preventing the thing from catching fire in the first place. So:

1. *Try not to be on fire.*
2. *If you are on fire, just let yourself be on fire, you'll eventually go out.*
3. *Rinse and repeat.*

Obviously good advice. Marginally better than *stop, drop and roll,* which is useless for anxiety sufferers but great for folks who are actually on fire. Although perhaps less eloquent than a Zen Buddhist, something in a Matt Haig book, or literally anything a trained professional might tell you in a session, this is—in its extreme essence—the advice I give myself these days. A very cooked-down version of years of therapy, self-help books, trainings, and personal reflections on the subject of so-called panic attacks (I hate the word 'attack', but more on that below).

I have been living with panic all my adult life. I was 18 the first time I really panicked. Like a lot of people, it took me a long while just to know what was going on, and even more time to get to a place where I can confidently tell myself, *you are on fire right now, but soon you won't be, and that will be nice.* And even sometimes, *oh look! A tiny fire. I'd better put it out before it consumes me!*

I wrote this tiny little book for myself: it's the sort of book I was looking for in my late teens when I was wondering what on earth was happening to me. It is not in any way meant to replace the advice of a licensed therapist (I'm in my fourth year of therapy now, and it has been important for my recovery) but it is meant to be carried with you to help in times of need. Like a brief *Hitchhiker's Guide...* to not panicking.

When Arthur Dent woke up on a Monday morning at his home in the English countryside, the furthest thing from his mind was that someone would try to demolish his house to make room for a freeway, or that miles above the planet's surface, aliens were preparing to demolish the Earth to make way for an intergalactic byway, or that finally, his best friend, Ford Prefect, was actually an alien, who was planning on rescuing him from utter annihilation by taking him on an intergalactic journey that would involve time travel, two-headed heads of state, and depressed robots. But that's how it is sometimes, and certainly how panic happens to many people: suddenly it's just there, and it feels huge, complex, tragic, comic… and truly world-shattering.

Arthur's bad morning is an apt metaphor for what we go through when we suffer from episodic anxiety and panic. It's surprising. It's out of the blue. It can feel disorienting—like someone pulled the rug out from under you, or like a bunch of bureaucratic aliens just blew up the planet you were standing on and now *ladies and gentlemen, you are floating in space.*

I've been there—I have been Arthur Dent. But now, fellow Arthurian, allow me to be your Ford Prefect. All you need is this guide. And a towel, of course.

5. The Next Episode

Perhaps the worst thing we could call the horrible, debilitating, surprising, breath-taking, panic-inducing phenomenon that overtakes more than a quarter of Americans at least once in life is a "panic attack". Using the word "attack" strikes me, after living with these things for the past fifteen years, as the exact wrong word to use. I prefer to think of it/them as "a panic" or "a panic episode" or "an episode of panic", because this is far more descriptive of what is actually happening, and helps me to focus on the most crucial aspect of a panic episode—that it is *episodic*—meaning that *it will end*. When we refer to it as an "attack", we are giving it too much power.

Panic episodes affect so many people in the US, and yet it seems like the culture is only now getting to the point where we're talking out loud about the terrors that so many of us experience. It still feels taboo. Maybe not so much online, but in real life, at work especially—it still feels dangerous to talk about mental health issues, much less take sick time to deal with them, because it might mean *something is wrong with us*. Well, there is probably something wrong with each and every one of us, and I'll bet you at least two dollars that there is 100 per cent something wrong with this culture, this economy, this country and this world, and that *(gasp!)* a lot of folks are having trouble keeping it together in the face of all the terrible things we are confronted with every day. Neuroscientists have, rather helpfully, figured out the mechanics of how this works in our brains, which goes a long way to explain why we might be losing our collective minds.

6. Three Brains

You think you have one brain, but you are wrong. You have three brains (four, if you include the weird bundle of neurons that live in our guts). Think of your brain as one of those wooden nesting dolls, where one is within the other, and then the other, until you get to the center. The innermost Russian doll of your brain is the 'reptile' brain. It controls automatic things, like breathing. It's the part of our brain that is responsible for our survival (great, thank you!) but also has a lot to do with panic episodes (go to hell, you monster).

One layer out from the lizard brain we have the 'mammalian' brain, home of the amygdala, which is constantly scanning for threats, or more accurately, is scanning the environment, using our senses, particularly sight, to look for anything... *unusual*. If it detects something out of the ordinary, it is programmed to send an alert to different parts of the brain. This alert happens in the form of stress hormones, which fire us up and trigger the 'fight or flight' impulse. The stress hormones alert the third brain, the 'neocortex', or as I call it, the 'Human Brain'.

The Human Brain is the part of our brain that does our *thinking*. It is the most-recently evolved part of the brain and is responsible for creativity, reason, our ability to plan—all the higher-order thinking skills. It is the brain you think about when you think about your brain: it is the left and right hemisphere, the outermost region that has all those little wrinkles. The Human Brain is the boss—or at least it should be. When the amygdala senses a threat and sends out stress hormones, the boss in our Human Brain gets the message first. Her job then is to receive the message (something is unusual!), figure out what that is (make a plan!), and then act (commit to the plan!). This is known as *executive function*, and it works most of the time for most of us. But sometimes it fails. And when it does, guess who picks up the slack? The reptilian brain.

Here's where things get tricky: if any of these processes doesn't work correctly, or gets overloaded by too much information, we can get episodes of panic. For example, the amygdala senses something strange happening, and the neocortex can't see anything strange, so it can't make a decision, and so the amygdala doesn't know to stop sounding the alarm, until the alarm is the only thing the brain is doing and—just like that—you are in a full-blown panic. You aren't being attacked. Nothing is wrong. You aren't having a stroke, or a heart attack, or an aneurysm, or a schizophrenic episode—nor are you having a psychic intuition about a horrible event that's about to unfold in the external world. You are having a communication problem between your three brains, who are just trying to keep you safe, but—unfortunately—failing miserably.

It helps me to think of these brains in a sort of anthropomorphic way. I picture the Reptile Brain as the lizard in the Walt Disney Animated version of *Alice in Wonderland*. You know—the Lizard with a Ladder? He's a jolly old fellow, happy to help out when the Dodo needs a ladder to see what's up with the giant Alice popping out of the house. Except for when he's spooked, then he runs away screaming. It's really funny. But that's the Reptile Brain. It chugs along. It's happy to help. Until you freak it out. Then it's like the Lizard with a Ladder.

The Mammalian Brain is like the White Rabbit. It's a bit nervous, always scanning for threats, and it is very sensitive, with its large ears, attuned to hear the tiniest crack of a leaf on the ground.. Hearing something it looks round, scans, and then resumes thumping along over the understory *(oh my whim and whiskers, I'm late, I'm late I'm late)*. If it hears a twig snap, and then identifies the threat, that Rabbit is outta there. You can picture the Lizard, with his ladder, riding the Rabbit straight to Wonderland.

Finally, I picture the Human Brain as Alice on her best day. Confident, calm, in a buoyant mood—on one of those days where nothing is wrong, and she feels the harmony of the universe humming along within each atom of her being. This is Alice post-Wonderland, perhaps. She's been through her Wonderland ordeal, and knows that at any moment, she could fall back down the Rabbit Hole. But if that *does* happen, she'll know just what to do, because Alice is the *boss*.

So I'm Alice, *the boss*, hanging out, being my boss self. The White Rabbit is out in the woods, hears a snap, is startled and alert. The Lizard with a Ladder passes by. The Rabbit asks, *did you make that sound?* The Lizard replies in his Disneyfied British accent: *not sure guvnah!*

The White Rabbit, growing concerned, hears another snap. Or at least he thinks he hears it.

> —Did you hear *that?*
> —I think I *did*, by gum! cries the Lizard.

And suddenly, as if pursued by the Queen of Hearts herself *(OFF with their HEADS!)* the White Rabbit is off, the Lizard and his Ladder in tow, running through the woods, screaming.

I see them coming. I look around, and yeah, I'm a little concerned because they're so concerned, and it's all a bit concerning. But I don't see the crazy Queen, or any other threat; it's a false alarm and so I say "Hey! Rabbit! Lizard! Cool it! Relax!" And, because I'm *the boss,* they do.

But it takes practice to get there, to the boss level, and sometimes, even still, the Rabbit and the Lizard don't listen to reason. In those moments, it's best to let them run/scream it out. And to remember that they are going to tire themselves out, in ten minutes or so. When that happens, I know to take myself on a brisk walk or to do something else very physical for a little while. I feel panic very squarely in my body, through my limbs and in my lungs, and pumping through my veins, and I find it helpful to let it be in my body—to take it for a walk or a bike ride or a jog. And you'll figure out what works best for you, how to best deal with your version of the Lizard with the Ladder and the White Rabbit.

7. April Fools

I had my first panic episode in what seemed like ages today. As is often the case, it was a surprise, and perhaps fitting that it happened on April Fools' Day while on a hike with my husband and our dog—a typically innocuous experience, and one of my favorite things to do on a perfect spring day. So what happened?

Two factors, I think, contributed to my episode, which was short-lived, thankfully, but exhausting nevertheless. First, it's the third or so week of shelter-in-place orders during the Covid-19 crisis. In other words, like everyone else on Earth, I have a lot of stress lurking beneath the surface. I'm one of the luckier ones: I can work at home, and although my husband works at a grocery store, he's exceedingly cautious and I'm not all that worried about our health or finances. All the same, this is a stressful and frightening time, and so people like me who live with anxiety must be extra mindful: stress is a trigger, or at least a catalyst for panic. It puts us on high alert, often subconsciously, and so our response to things that would normally be tolerable can be a bit exaggerated. So what was the actual trigger, then? What was the event that triggered this episode?

Sometimes I forget that I have a physiological response to heights, and this particular path, which I hadn't been on in years, is staggeringly high up. The views are incredible, and yet—for someone with a bit of vertigo lurking in the periphery—this can be overwhelming. The panic came on slowly; I was aware of it, I sort of watched it unfold, even to the point where I told myself (and my husband) that I was having a bit of trouble, but that I wanted to push through. That's when things got unbearable.

A quarter of a mile or so later, the sensations that I was experiencing—vertigo, for me, is very visual and cognitive: things begin to look strange and stretched-out, like adding a fish-eye lens to a camera—started doing things to my thinking that are hard to describe. A slightly dissociative feeling starts to well inside me, and, before I know it, I think: something is wrong, I'm going to pass out, I'm having a stroke. That's the moment when things turn from a feeling of vertigo to a full-blown panic.

I had to stop. I had to turn around. I had to get back to the car as *quickly as possible.*

And so I did. And I told myself that I would be alright, in ten or so minutes, or just as soon as we got back to the car.

And I was.

But wow—it's still surprising how panic can take you so quickly, a riptide threatening to pull you under. And like swimming against a strong current, once you are free of it, back on shore, the exhaustion is inexplicable.

It's frustrating to have things like a pleasant afternoon walk turn into a nightmare. Even when you know you'll survive, and you know you'll eventually be all right, it is still unnerving and just downright annoying to modify what you are doing feeling like it *won*.

I think it's important to acknowledge this feeling: sometimes it does get the better of you. But don't dwell. Sit with the feeling for the rest of the afternoon—take it easy—and then get back to your life.

8. Negative Capability

Anxiety and panic are chameleon-like in their ability to dress up as something else. I've already mentioned this, but it is this characteristic of anxiety and panic that has been, for me, the most frustrating, and is, for many of us who deal with these issues, the thing that most frequently lands us in an Urgent Care or Emergency Room.

A sudden, stabbing pain in your chest grips you with no advance warning: what do you do? Well, we've all been told *ad nauseum* that this is a classic sign of a heart attack, so we rush off the ER.

We wait. We are seen. And the EKG? Shows nothing.

When the doctor pokes their head in to debrief us, well... we are used to that look on their face by now, aren't we? That sort of sickly sympathetic (not empathetic) expression, which silently communicates to us:

Nothing's wrong, dear: you're just crazy.

Let me tell you a story. The first time I landed in the emergency room due to panic and anxiety was back in 2012. In hindsight, I'm surprised I made it as long as I did without a visit, although this was when I was approaching 30, and to be sure even I, chronic anxiety and panic-haver, was blessed with a sense of invincibility in my 20s (I mean, as long as I wasn't in an airplane, on a bridge, in a building over two stories tall, riding a train or in the near vicinity of a major metropolitan area). In my 20s I didn't think about my health and was certain I would die in one of the above scenarios; that something big and bad was headed my way, but perhaps I could outrun it, or avoid it. As I inched towards 30 all of that began to shift.

I became hyperaware of my body, and began to worry excessively about my heart, but also my head—my brain. I thought of all the ways I might die *suddenly:* a stroke, a giant undiscovered tumor, a pulmonary embolism. Of course this was all possible. But equally true: *worrying about it only does so much good.* I knew that I could live a healthy lifestyle, and honestly I pretty much did (save for the odd bender). My worry had a limit and I blew through that—my Reptile Brain deciding that it needed to maintain vigilance 24 hours a day.

I was at band practice at a studio in Oakland. A safe place for me, usually; I went there frequently. But something felt off that day. Even when I left our apartment in Santa Cruz, I remember thinking that I wanted to wear a nice pair of socks in case something happened. A lyric from a Sunset Rubdown song ghosted through my mind as I got ready:

I hope that you die / in a decent pair of shoes / you gotta lotta long walking to do / where are you going / to?

My subconscious—so complicit in my misery.

As band practice went on my heart rate went up. Makes sense—when I sing I really belt it out, and I play guitar pretty aggressively, too. Mine was a loud, grungy, indie band. I *always* broke a sweat, and when we played live, I would be positively *dripping* by the end.

So what was different this time? *Something,* I decided. I knew that there was something wrong. It was a gut feeling. I told the guys I was feeling "off," and that I wanted to go to the doctor. They knew me. They looked concerned. But they were supportive, which is the correct way to handle this.

I left, determined to see a doctor, safely back in Santa Cruz. *Just to make sure.* I stopped at the Rite Aid at 51st and Telegraph, a few blocks from where I used to live in the Temescal neighborhood, another place that felt safe and familiar. I decided I'd get some aspirin and water, *just in case.* You know, in case I was having a very small and painless heart attack, or was about to have one, the only symptom of which was a quick heartbeat after doing strenuous exercise! I don't make the rules, as they say: I just obey the panic.

I'm in Rite Aid. I've got my aspirin and water, then it *hits:* that insane rush that any panic sufferer knows and what is often described, officially, as "an overwhelming sense of doom."

Holy shit that's an understatement.

It comes screaming in at Mach 5, a Blue Angel during Fleet Week. I can feel the sonic boom of the adrenalin, rushing in to meet this unholy threat to save the day.

This is all happening. Inside of me. Standing in line at Rite Aid.

I am *really* good at hiding the fact that I'm having a panic attack, experiencing anxiety, or that I'm just really unhappy when I'm in public, but my practiced defenses were no match for this. I turned a shade of sickly grey, started doing a weird dance that I often do when I panic, and then, thinking *this is it—the heart attack!* I opened the aspirin bottle, which naturally exploded all over the floor, scooped two up, pounded them down with the water, steadily drawing a small crowd of onlookers from a safe distance—this was Telegraph Avenue in Oakland, after all, people did far stranger things on the quarter hour—and at the peak of my freakout, a voice called to me across an unnavigable expanse:

Next, please.

I made eye contact with the cashier. He did not seem to notice that I was about to die.

How strange. But then, we can never truly know anyone, can we?

I put the bottle of water and the empty bottle of aspirin on the counter. I croaked out, *Can you please call an ambulance?* And he was like, *what?* I repeated myself. He said, *Are you sure?* I screamed at him: I'*m fucking having a heart attack call a fucking ambulance!*

That did the trick.

He called 911, I talked to a dispatcher, she sighed knowingly—people who are having heart attacks usually aren't as riled up as I was!—but sent some paramedics anyway.

And 30 minutes later—what a long heart attack I was having!—a couple of very nice EMTs showed up, did an EKG, said there *might* be something funny with it, but that I definitely *wasn't* having any issues at the moment, and that I could choose whether or not to go to the ER, or make an appointment with my own doctor later. I still thought I was dying, so opted for the ER. I just could not fathom that what had just happened to me was "just in my head", as so, so many of us experience when we have our first *big one.*

I texted something extremely dramatic to my husband, who was only my boyfriend at the time and stupidly young. A farewell, perhaps, like *tell my mother I'll miss her. Don't forget to feed the cat.* Maybe even a last will and testament.

At the Highland Hospital ER I was deposited, on a gurney, into a little closet-like room. I waited. For an hour. Two hours. Longer. Of course, I was still alive, which felt oddly anticlimactic. I was *really* tired, because a giant dose of adrenaline will do that to you, but other than that, I was just… bored.

Someone came and did another EKG and then I waited for another few hours. People with all sorts of emergencies were wheeled by. I saw a guy who had been shot! They had bigger fish to fry. That's when the doctor appeared, finally, to discuss my results. We'll call him Dan, but I have no idea what his name was; only that his name badge clearly read "INTERN." I had no health insurance and did not actually care who he was, only a wish that he'd break the news of my pending demise gently.

"Your EKG was fine," he said robotically. "Totally normal. There's nothing wrong with you… or at least with your heart."

I braced myself: what had they discovered? The tumor?

"Have you done something recently that you feel guilty about?" he asked.

I thought about this for a moment.

No, I had not, other than being vaguely ashamed of my sexuality and body, worried about my overconsumption of gasoline on my weekly trips to Oakland, and my chronic lack of money.

But I wouldn't say *guilty*. I said as much.

"Well, I think you've just had a panic attack," he said. "They usually happen when someone feels guilty about something. You should see someone about getting medication, but for now, we'll send you home with some Ativan, in case it happens again."

Hello Ativan, my old friend.

I was numb at this point, and my boredom, cultivated from sitting in a dark room by myself with no phone, book, or stimuli of any sort for nine hours, had blossomed into the only rational emotional response available: *I don't give a shit, just let me drive home now.* And I did. Along with my jug of drugs.

The point of this story, aside from its sheer comedic value, is twofold. First, I wanted to share this story to firmly illustrate how panic, especially to the novice, can feel like being hit by a motherfucking train. If you know, you know, as they say. Second: the attending ER *intern* said the dumbest fucking shit I've ever heard anyone say about panic and anxiety ever in a long history of living with this, reading about it, talking with others about it and all the rest.

WAS I FEELING GUILTY ABOUT SOMETHING?

Seriously?

For the uninitiated, this is a good example of what not to say to someone who has just gone through an episode. Because first, *what?* But second, because there is no single determinant of what causes a panic episode to occur, and it certainly isn't the fault of the person suffering one. In fact, as far as I can tell, the jury is still out on what is happening in our brains and bodies. There are theories, sure, but that's it. But here's the hard truth:

> Nothing causes panic episodes, or I should say: no *thing*.
>
> Or I should say, there isn't always a discernable trigger;
> they sometimes just happen *for no discernable reason at all.*

It's a terrible thought, but it's made it so much simpler: there doesn't need to be a reason. I just panic sometimes.

Seriously: it's liberating. That panic just happens means that I'm *not* dying.

True, it means that it could happen again, and to be completely honest, it likely will. But when it *does* come, I know that it's just a feeling now, a very powerful one, like jealousy, for example: it can feel all-consuming sometimes, and sometimes it can feel like the nothing of a breeze through an open window. But it will *pass.*

The work becomes learning to accept uncertainty, which brings us to the larger point. The British romantic poet John Keats famously wrote about the concept of "negative capability" in a now-famous letter to his brothers:

> … it struck me what quality went to form a Man of Achievement, especially in Literature, and which Shakespeare possessed so enormously—I mean Negative Capability, that is, when a man is capable of being in uncertainties, mysteries, doubts, without any irritable reaching after fact and reason…

Of course, Keats is mostly talking about literature, especially poetry, but the idea is applicable to all sorts of endeavors, and particularly to the art of living with panic and anxiety, I think. It's hard medicine, friends, but there is no cure.

However, like Keats, we can develop our ability to be in life's "uncertainties, mysteries, doubts, without"—and this is the crucial piece for us—"any irritable reaching after fact and reason". Once we accept that panic and anxiety are inevitable conditions, or features of life (for everyone, I think to varying degrees, but perhaps especially to us, the chosen ones), and that panic episodes come and go without always having discernable reasons, then we have come a long way towards freedom from their tyranny. Yes, true enough, we'll never be truly free, but for my money, there is serious liberatory potential in freeing one's self from the fetters of cause and effect, at least when it comes to panic and anxiety.

These days, when I have a panic episode, I still let it burn out, but I don't spend much time investigating the cause of the blaze. I might feel a bit curious about how that fire started, but instead of worrying about it too much, I very consciously focus my attention on helping it along: usually I do some polyvagal breathing, and distract myself with some tedious little chore—the dishes, folding some clothes, data entry—the more rote and monotonous, the better. Or sometimes, when the feeling is very physical, as it was this morning, I will take some ibuprofen and *just dance it out*.

And you know what?
It works.

I'm still alive, writing these words.

9. Breathing

Breathing is miraculous. We are, from the moment we are born, always breathing.

In.
Out.
In.
Out.

I am breathing right now, as I write this, comfortably through my nose. And you too are breathing as you read this, maybe also through your nose, or perhaps through your mouth due to some sinus problem, or perhaps you are a little focused on your breath and you are breathing in through your nose and out through your mouth. Regardless of how you are doing it, you are breathing: you are taking in oxygen from the atmosphere of the Earth deep into your lungs, wonder of wonders, which then use the oxygen molecules to oxygenate your blood, chemically converting it to carbon dioxide, which you then breathe out into the atmosphere, which is absorbed by plants, converted back into oxygen, and released back into the atmosphere, where it will be breathed in by someone else.

A miracle.

And this is happening to you, right now, and will continue, even after you go to sleep. Another miracle.

Our bodies are equipped with an autonomic nervous system, which does things like tell our lungs to keep breathing in and out even when we are not thinking about it. After all, how often are you thinking about breathing? Maybe, at most, once or twice a day, for people who practice meditation or mindfulness. But for most, probably almost never. That's okay. Your body does quite a lot of thinking for you, so you can think about other things— enjoying yourself, or getting some work done, or spending time with your dog, or cat, or kids, or eating, or sleeping.

One great thing about breathing is that you know if you are doing it, you are still alive. This can be useful when you are panicking—it can be something to hold on to, to focus on, to help get you through. Even if what you are panicking about is breathing-related, as it so often is for a lot of us. Things are going fine, then a ghost of a not-feeling sneaks up on us; followed by *I can't breathe;* a perceived shortness of breath; another thought, perhaps *I'm going to pass out* or I*'m going to stop breathing and die;* more sensations of breathlessness and before you know you are in a panic.

Good news: I have had lots and lots of panic attacks. I have never once stopped breathing. I have never once died.

In fact, to my knowledge, there are absolutely zero documented cases of folks dying as a result of panic. That really is something to hold on to. Panic typically peaks after 10 minutes or less. Ten minutes. And during all that time, which can feel like a lot longer than 10 minutes, you are still breathing, still changing oxygen to carbon dioxide, in and out, without even trying, and so even in that terrible place of suffering and pain, you are still performing miracles.

10. Practicing

Start a practice. Any practice.

I love the word *practice*. It calls to mind the practice of doctor, or the practice of a therapist, but also yoga practice, meditation practice. I have several practices going myself, which I attend to sometimes more and sometimes less, but I keep at them: I practice them.

Most mornings I practice meditation for 15 or 20 minutes, make a cup of coffee, then take up either writing or reading, sometimes both. I love these practices, especially in the mornings, which I claim for myself. It took me a while, but I started practicing waking up a couple of hours early to carve out time for my practices before work. Of course, there was an adjustment period—developing new habits takes a couple of months to really stick, according to neuroscientists—but once I got there, I really began to appreciate the time I gave to my practices.

You might start yoga, or mindfulness, or a mindful yoga practice. Or perhaps your practice will be walking around the block, through the park, or in open nature. Maybe your practice will be an art, like drawing, painting, or practicing music (another of mine). Practice helps us develop creativity and gives us a routine, two things our brains and bodies really love. It feels good to have something to work on, something that connects mind and body— that helps us grow and keeps us nicely attuned to a *rhythm*.

And it's okay to skip practice sometimes. Or for your practice to lapse. You can pick up a practice and you put it down again—it's yours. Do what you like with it.

11. Feeling

So much of what causes us to panic has to do with unconscious process—the three brains making, unbeknownst to us, perceive something unfamiliar and *voila*—panic. But sometimes anxiety and panic are fueled by things we feel: a skipped heartbeat, a sensation that we can't breathe, a shooting pain in the head, or loss of feeling in a toe. These things can all trigger a panic episode. The worst, for me, are the things that happen while sleeping.

I was dreaming, which I generally enjoy doing. I was on some sort of ship: I think a cruise ship, but maybe a cruise ship in space? It's uncertain. At some point during this cruise, I felt my chest tighten, a knot in a muscle deep in there. I'm still dreaming, by the way. In the dream, I try to find a bathroom, a strategy I often employ when I'm on the verge of freaking out in waking life. I get to the bathroom, but there is water everywhere, filling the tub, the sink, spilling onto the floor, filling the small room. That's when I woke up.

The knot in my chest was still there.

Sigh.

I think of myself as an old pro when it comes to things like this—but every once in a while, something catches me off guard, like this knot. I remember all the things I've learned about myself, anxiety, and panic; remind myself that this is not anything *but* that.

Because *feelings are powerful.*

Our imaginations are so powerful that they can create what psychologists call "psychic equivalence"—a feeling that something you've imagined is not imagined, but *one hundred percent real*. It is what happens when you feel that skipped heartbeat and *know*, within a second, that you are having a heart attack. Or when you are on an airplane, feel a little turbulence, and *know* that the plane is going to crash. We have a thought—*the plane is going to crash*—and it instantly becomes possible.

The fact that this is not how most people operate was news to me. I just assumed everyone was this way. But guess what: other people think the thought "the plane is going to crash", and then, another, more reasonable part of them, says "probably not". And that's *that*.

Related to psychic equivalence is the term "catastrophic thoughts" or "catastrophic thinking". This is the habit of jumping from Point A to Point *Wereallgoingtodieohmy God!*.

Key here is the idea of habit: catastrophic thinking is a habit. It also serves a purpose: it is protective. It is our way of perennially preparing for the worst, of trying to assert control in the chaos of our lives. Expecting the worst serves so many functions that it is oddly hard to quit doing. This is a great paradox that is painful, yet powerful to realize: our anxiety is helping us to feel safe. And the more we practice it, the more true it becomes, which is why symptoms tend to get worse with avoidance. I like to visualize my brain having this conversation:

> Lizard: *[Feeling turbulence]* What was that?
> Rabbit: *[Nodding aggressively]* I'll tell you what that was: that was the feeling of this whole plane going straight down.
> Alice: Fellas, relax. It's probably just…
> Lizard: YOU DON'T KNOW WHAT YOU'RE TALKING ABOUT.
> Rabbit: Did you feel THAT? That's the engine failing. We're *dead*.
> Alice: Oh no… what are we gonna do? There's nowhere to go!
> Lizard: Oh no, oh no, oh no, oh no…
> Rabbit: HAIL MARY FULL OF GRACE…

Alice, who began in control, is overpowered by the Lizard and the Rabbit. And that's okay. I find that my inner Alice *does* lose control from time to time, even after loads of practice, therapy, and the self-awareness that I've spent a decade cultivating. But every time she loses control, she gets it back. And she gets a bit stronger.

Remember how, in *Alice in Wonderland*, it takes Alice a while to get the hang of the rules of Wonderland? How to talk to the various creatures she encounters, how much of which side of the mushroom to eat, and so on? This has been my experience with panic: it's taken a while to figure out how the rules, but it *is* possible to figure them out.

One trick for me has been learning how to talk to my White Rabbit and my Lizard. I used to be very stern with them, sometimes I'd even sort of yell. This seemed to work: anger and aggression can feel really powerful, and do tend to quiet people down sometimes. But with the guidance of my therapist, I figured out that talking to myself this way just wasn't cutting it.

I'm trying out being a kinder Alice, reassuring the White Rabbit and the Lizard, very gently, almost like talking to a child. I tell them it's okay. I tell them that I'll protect them, and that they can relax. I say, *thanks for looking out for us, but I can take it from here.* I acknowledge that they are there to help, I thank them, I reassure them, and then I move on.

12. Meditating

I've had several periods in my life that I think of as "peak anxiety" times. I've already described a bit of my life during the first panic episode that landed me in the ER. My day job at that time was working as a substitute teacher's aide at an elementary school, and on my worst days I would lock myself in the bathroom several times a day, trying to hold myself together.

One day, after a horrible day of panic at work, I didn't know what to do. I couldn't keep the thoughts in my head straight, couldn't stop worrying, couldn't stop expecting to drop dead.

A thought struck me, which stopped the noise for a minute: the idea that I should just sit in a chair, close my eyes, and focus on my breathing. I did so. I closed my eyes and focused on breathing in, breathing out. If I started thinking about something else, I just went back to my breath. Over and over. Until I felt the most novel feeling: stillness.

(Long exhale).

I didn't know it then, but I had just sat and meditated. Later, when I formally learned Transcendental Meditation, I felt validated both in my choice to learn that particular technique, but also in honoring my instinct; regularly practiced meditation is one of the most effective tools humans have in living with anxiety, panic, and depression.

I still feel slightly awkward saying "I practice meditation" or "I'm gonna go meditate for twenty minutes" out loud. I'm not sure why. Millions and millions of people meditate regularly. There are mindfulness meditators. There are yogic meditators. There are Zen meditators. There are Transcendental meditators. Whatever the method, millions of people, and the wisdom traditions they adhere to, agree that meditation is a worthwhile practice.

I came to meditation through art via my fascination with the filmmaker David Lynch and his book *Catching the Big Fish*, which describes Lynch's experience with Transcendental Meditation and how it relates to his creative practice. Lynch's narrative rang true for me. After a lot of hesitation, I found a teacher and learned how to meditate. It didn't work. Not right away. This is why I think there are so many skeptics when it comes to the effectiveness of meditating in dealing with anxiety and panic. It isn't a silver bullet; it doesn't work overnight.

But it *does* work for millions of people—myself included. Over the years I've cultivated meditation as a practice and as something I keep in my toolkit. It works really well preventatively, and also, can calm me right down in a panicky pinch. It's a bit like growing a plant from seed though: it may take a while to sprout, and then another while to grow, and another while to really bloom. But the blossom is worth the water and patience required.

13. Connecting

We're told everything is connected, and that's inescapably true: we carry massively powerful tiny computers in our pockets connected to the internet, and therefore other people, reminding us of this fact by pinging us with tiny red notifications every few seconds. We're more connected than we've ever been and paradoxically feeling more alone than ever. What is going on?

This is no accident. Just like the beauty, diet, and advertising industries exist to make people feel inadequate, and therefore we 'need' to purchase products to become adequate, social media companies exploit our fear of missing out, and this is making us feel extremely lonely.

I'll be the first to raise my hand and say I actively contribute to the problem. Every time I post a video of a party I'm giving, or some other fun social event to my Instagram Story, I am, in effect, probably making somebody else—someone that I probably care about!—feel like garbage. Maybe I forgot to invite them to the party, or maybe they are living abroad this year, or maybe they are stuck at work... it doesn't matter. My post makes them feel more alone. And you know what? That makes me feel more alone, too. I don't need to prove this to know that it's true.

What to do?

We must be intentional about connecting to people in real life. The people who are directly in front of us, for starters. When was the last time you met that old friend just for coffee and a chat or a game of chess? Or struck up a conversation with a stranger?

Here's a little story.

I'm out walking my dog, Millie. It's Christmas Eve in my small suburban town, chilly but pleasant. The pepper trees lining my neighborhood streets dropped their tiny red peppercorns all over the pavement. They crunch under my feet. The red combined with the willowy, green boughs of the tree are doing quite a good job at making me feel festive.

Millie and I encounter a postal worker. We actually saw him a few blocks back. It being Christmas Eve, I took out my earbuds and said "thanks for delivering the mail today," to which he replied, "Oh, it's my pleasure." A real Mr. Rogers moment. This second encounter was even better. He reaches into his mail bag and produces a puppy snap for Millie. We chat. Nothing particularly memorable was said, but walking away, I feel energized.

This little moment had such an electrical force! We connected. And wow—I think we often forget how healing, energizing, and balancing simple interactions can be.

And of course, these interactions are sometimes virtual. During the pandemic we all had to re-define what social interaction is. It took a while for me, but I realized, along with countless others, that virtual interaction was better than no interaction. A gathering of friends on Zoom or Facetime, while not quite as good as the real thing, helped replicate the feeling of social connectedness that we need to stay healthy. Sort of like a sun lamp helps people with seasonal affective disorder. It's not the sun! But it'll do!

Even if your only option is a phone call, or better yet, a video chat—do it. You'll feel better.

14. Moving

My husband was depressed. For a long time. We didn't quite realize it, but he was. It happened stealthily, as many mental health conditions often do. Before you realize they are happening... there they are.

Depression is not anxiety, but the two are often connected in how they relate to the body, how they take the body hostage, use it as a host. Depression and anxiety sap our energy, leave us depleted. Have you noticed that the stronger your anxiety or depression become, the weaker and less in control you feel?

One powerful way to fight anxiety is through moving your body. This can take any form you like, but the key is to move.

Upon the suggestion of his therapist (they *do* have good ideas sometimes), my husband went in search of a hobby—something to get him out of his own head. For my husband, this meant rekindling a love of skateboarding, something he hadn't done since he was a teenager. I think it was sort of a happy accident that one of the hobbies he decided to try was something as kinetic and active as skating, but I'm so glad this happened. Physical exertion releases endorphins that make us feel better, happier. By combining something that requires skill and practice with something that gets the heart rate up and makes you sweat is a genius way of dealing with depression and anxiety. It's like taking a multivitamin designed to boost mental health.

He gets exercise for his physical body as well as his mental state. He focuses on learning new tricks, which is good for his brain and self-confidence; following the theory of multiple intelligences, body-kinesthetic is one of his best and has been neglected since he was a teen. Exercising this intelligence is actually helping him feel smarter.

He likes to make videos of himself doing tricks, which he shares on social media. This is one of those cases where social media can actually be a good thing: people who've known him for decades were *amazed* at seeing the wild tricks he was doing on a skateboard. I mean people just had no idea he could do things like that, and they let him know! All that positive attention reinforced the positive feelings surrounding getting out of the house, out of his own head, and moving his body.

For you, this might look completely different. It does for me. One thing I do is dance. I put on my favorite record and just go for it. Usually alone. I like to spin around a lot. Even for a few minutes, around the house, I find this makes a difference. I do not like to share this with people. It's just something for me that feels good and that I have *zero* need to share with the world (you're welcome). I also hike, because I live in a place that affords me that luxury. I bike to work. I lift weights either at the gym or at home.

I have definitely found that finding a gym or hiking partner is really motivating, especially one who is more fit than me—this also ticks that connection box. I have a younger friend who, one summer, helped me get over my fear of lifting weights. A silly fear, perhaps, but I just couldn't imagine myself doing it. I worried I'd have a stroke or an embolism or... you know the drill. I was also afraid that people would judge my body, judge me—that I, a non-gym-person, did not belong with those Real Gym People.

I bit the bullet, went with him, and let myself feel all these things. Over the course of a month, I felt more comfortable lifting weights, with being in the gym around other people. Every day that I didn't have a medical emergency while engaged in the troublingly named motions of a dead lift was a small victory—a neurological reinforcement.

I had more energy after gym days, was in a better mood, felt lighter and less anxious. But I want to be completely honest: sometimes while working out I felt a tiny bit light-headed and *hoo boy!* that can really trigger an episode. Or sometimes, if I'm having a stressful time and the gym is packed with people, it can feel overwhelming. I take it as it comes on those days. Sometimes it's too much and I bail. But I make sure to tell myself, *that's all right, kid. Get back on the horse tomorrow.*

Other times I work through it, knowing that I'll feel better in just a little while if I do.

And I always do.

15. Fear-ing

Almost everything I read about anxiety and panic has to do with getting *away* from anxiety and panic. Articles tell you how to move *beyond* panic, how to get *rid* of panic, how to *remove* any and all feelings of anxiety. Of course, anyone who has struggled with this stuff knows that when it's bad, the only thing we want is to *feel normal again*. But what if "normal" doesn't exist; what if feeling normal is just a myth? What if feeling anxiety is a part of how we are actually *supposed* to feel?

I know, I know. You don't want to feel anxious, and you certainly don't want to feel panicky. You don't want those heart palpitations just like you don't want vertigo, or feeling like your soul is leaving your body, or amnesia. But perhaps these feelings—which we are so quick to write off as maladaptive, a malfunctioning of our nervous system—serve a less obvious, deeper purpose?

Well before the advent of neuroscience, and our remarkable 21st century ability to easily peer inside our own brains (talk about metacognition!), writers and philosophers grappled with the problem of anxiety. In grad school, my professor, John Hampsey, taught an excellent class on existentialist thought in Western lit, and this broad overview really helped me tune in to the fact that people have been struggling with the anxiety and panic of existence since Biblical times. Here's a bit of an outline, and for more find his book *Paranoia and Contentment*.

In *Ecclesiastes*, the book in the Bible that gave us the song "Turn, Turn, Turn," among other persistent, ancient memes, the anonymous author struggles with the anxiety of being aware of the finitude of existence.

Thousands of years later, Danish philosopher Soren Kierkegaard spent his entire life writing about anxiety. Here things get interesting: Kierkegaard wasn't trying to figure out a way to get *over* anxiety; he was trying to figure out what it was *for*.

For Kierkegaard, anxiety wasn't something to run away from, it was something essential to being human—something central to our *existence*. Kierkegaard, and other philosophers and writers, including Albert Camus and Jean-Paul Sartre, felt that we're all anxious about our very existence, but to truly experience anything—to really *feel* things—*we need to feel anxious*. It's literally what makes us human, makes us capable of creativity, it is actually what *life* is. Without anxiety, we literally have nothing. For Kierkegaard, and later Martin Heidegger, *et al*, anxiety is a necessary component of human creativity.

In pop culture, we often think of the cliché of the moody, beret-clad, cigarette-smoking *French* existential artist-type. You know them. They can be found lounging in a cafe, with a seemingly endless supply of trust-fund wealth, wallowing in self-pity. This is directly related to the misconception that "real art" always comes from the pain of the tortured artist—it's the kernel of truth at the center of the stereotype.

This isn't to say that art only comes from pain, or something equally as base, but that at the base of our existence, at the bottom of the everything, is this beautiful uncertainty that hovers over the abyss, over life and death, which forces us to choose: create or fade into non-being. Do something or risk becoming utterly nothing. It's this deep, often subconscious fear of nothingness that propels us to be creative beings, the philosophers tell us. Certainly it's an interesting thought—with a ring of truth, for me.

Could this perception of anxiety's purpose change how you feel about your own? For me, it makes it easier to live with, transforms anxiety from something to fear to an object of utter curiosity, a fuel that propels me *towards* my creativity, which makes it far more tolerable. Instead of running *from* anxiety, or slamming the door in its face, I want to keep it at a safe distance, and study it. *Understand* it.

A former therapist of mine, who was into both mindfulness and somatic or body-oriented therapy, would talk about the *zone of tolerance* and the *zone of stimulation*, which is basically the idea that we all have set levels of how much stress and anxiety we can tolerate, and then we have upper limits, and outer limits. He said it can be effective to widen our zone of tolerance through confronting and "being with" the feelings that live outside of the zone. For me, this is re-envisioning my own anxiety, not as an external threat, but as an essential part of my being. This makes it easier to sit with, and grow more comfortable with. This knowledge is an olive branch: I'm inviting anxiety into my home and asking it to stay a while. What new, bizarre things can it show me? What might it help me create next?

16. Caring

When we think about *caring*, we think about others. As we should. I always think about what Kurt Vonnegut says: "We're here to help each other get through whatever this thing is." But in order to help others, we must take care of ourselves. I'm going to turn here to "self-care" or something akin to it, but by this I don't mean splurging on a massage, having a night in with rosé and a facial or any of that (although that's all perfectly fine—go for it). The self-care I'm talking about is a little less expensive, but harder to come by: self-love.

We tend to be hard on ourselves, often in ways that we don't realize. I am my own worst critic. Here's a list:

- Too fat
- Haven't accomplished enough
- Not enjoying yourself enough
- Selfish
- Not kind enough
- Don't work hard enough
- Lazy, generally
- Hypocritical
- Judgmental
- Afraid of life
- Too in my own head

This list could *go on*. But that's the point. I suspect that many of you hear these same voices whispering this shit to you constantly. *It's exhausting.*

It's exhausting to listen to, to defend yourself against (how absurd to have to defend yourself against yourself). It saps you of the self-love you deserve when you believe these things.

So here's a radical possibility: maybe that little voice is bullshit!

Maybe you are absolutely fine the way you are. Folks call this "radical acceptance" and, yes, in this world feeling okay about yourself is extremely radical. Consider how much money is made by corporations that depend on you feeling very shitty about yourself. The brands that thrive on your misery, on your FOMO[1]; the industries that turn a profit off your feeling like

---

[1] "Fear of missing out". See earlier reference to how social media is Some Bullshit.

garbage. Everything from your favorite cosmetic line to fucking Domino's, because where would they even be if we all weren't stress-eating carbs at midnight on a Tuesday?

What to do about this? Don't have the answer. Sorry.

But I'll tell you what: occasionally I feel a glimmer of what it might be like to like myself (we'll start with like and move towards *love*). I'll have a moment, usually when I'm alone, where I feel good about myself and think, "maybe I'm fine *right now*", and even better, "maybe everything else is okay for now, too". Usually this happens in conjunction with some other human. For example, during a slumpy, depressive week recently, two things happened: I got an email from a work colleague that lifted my spirits. It was complimentary, made me feel good, because someone recognized things about myself at work that I'm proud of. Later I went to the gym with a friend. I almost didn't go. But I did.[2]. At the end of that day, I had a glass of wine (okay, I had two. Ish) and one of those overwhelmingly nice "everything right now is okay, and actually I'm just fine the way I am, aren't I?" feelings.

What a *relief.*

Of course, there is a lot going on, but it is *possible* to have that feeling, and I think if it's possible to have it once, it's possible to cultivate. What a fantastic way to push back against what I believe to be a major force behind not only depression but also anxiety and panic: that we aren't good enough.

You can figure out how to care about yourself, to the point where at least occasionally, you can see the forest for the trees and understand that you *are* enough, that you don't need to change a fucking *thing* about yourself, and therefore, you can relax a little, as a treat. You can let go of that dense, dark, ball of stress you've been holding onto for dear life. A bit.

You can have a little rest.

---

2   AND I felt much better. See the chapter on *Moving.*

16. Loving

Love, love, love. Love is all you need. Yes, we know. I think the idea that "love" is a universal force of good is well-established.

Okay. But what does love have to do with panic?

I want to focus on 'love' as both a practice and as a chemical reaction, how the cultivation of this chemical reaction can help to keep us balanced. And because human love is complicated, I'm going to talk about my dog, Millie.

I love her. And part of why I love her is just science.

You've probably heard of the chemical *oxytocin*. It's what scientists believe is responsible for love in all its forms: parental love for children, romantic love between partners, and yes, love between humans and their companion animals. Interacting with your pet, scientists show, can release oxytocin in both you and your pet in doses that are like those found in human relationships. When you play with your dog, pet her, just chilling or gazing into each other's eyes, oxytocin is produced. This is great news for panic-sufferers.

My panic is deeply rooted in post-traumatic stress and attachment issues. A rough patch in my early childhood echoes into my adulthood. A common story. It is important for my mental health to ensure I'm getting enough oxytocin, which can be an issue for people with PTSD or folks with attachment issues.

So I pet my dog, and I play with her, and I spend loads of time looking into her eyes. Here, you give it a try:

I bet you're feeling better already.

17. Being

You've maybe seen this image, snapped by the NASA voyager satellite in 1990 and re-processed by NASA in 2020. Here's what NASA has to say about it:

> *The Pale Blue Dot* is a photograph of Earth taken February 14, 1990, by NASA's Voyager 1 at a distance of 3.7 billion miles (6 billion kilometers) from the Sun. The image inspired the title of scientist Carl Sagan's book, *Pale Blue Dot: A Vision of the Human Future in Space* in which he wrote: 'Look again at that dot. That's here. That's home. That's us.'

I don't have much to say about this except for that, sometimes, when I'm feeling overwhelmed, I think of myself on the tiny dot, and the Jon Brion song "Little Person" floats into my head, and I kind of relax:

> *I'm just a little person*
> *One person in a sea*
> *Of many little people*
> *Who are not aware of me.*

Depending on the sort of person you are, thinking like this can be a comfort, or perhaps even more anxiety-inducing (by all means, skip ahead if that's you!). Personally, I find a lot of comfort in feeling like I'm really a tiny being on a tiny planet. I don't know why, but I think it has to do with feeling like I'm on the level with all of my fellow creatures.

Once I was having a rather apocalyptic panic episode, where I was convinced that a nuclear strike was imminent. The thought that calmed me was the idea that I was just one person of about 7 billion people. I repeated it to myself like a mantra, and my panic subsided. So perhaps there's some power in this—just feeling like a little person on a planet of many little people.

Another cosmic image that helps me is from the James Webb Space Telescope. It's called *Deep Field No. 1* and according to NASA, all of the contents of this photo fit into a swatch of sky about the size of a grain of sand.

Talk about feeling tiny.

Take it all in, and feel as small as you need to feel in the face of all this wonder.

18. Non-Being

"Alright already, we all float on."

—Modest Mouse, "Float On"

At the root of all this panicking is, for me, a fear of death: of not *being* anymore. I've decided to do something about it. The not being part, I mean. There isn't much you can do about the actual dying part.

I talked with my therapist about this, and I definitely recommend having a therapist who's a phone call away. This is really the big scary thing for me and so it is important to feel supported.

What does *non-being* mean? It means that when we die, our consciousness goes out like a light. I absolutely hate this idea.

Even as I write this, my palms are sweating, and I feel a little stabbing pain in my chest.

I pause. I breathe a little. I keep writing.

When I started thinking about non-being seriously, really probing *why* 'not-existing' scared me so much, I found interesting results. One thing people often ask about fear of death is why be afraid of 'nothing'? There was *nothing* before you were born; won't you be in that same *nothing* when you die?

Huh.

I honestly don't know. *Maybe?*

For me, that's an okay thought. A little Band-Aid on a serious wound. But let's really think about what this void is.

My therapist recommended I check out some guided meditations on death as another way to get to the center of what was was bothering me. I did a few of these via YouTube.

Here's what I found.

They are really sort of grisly. In most of these meditations, you sort of imagine yourself laying in an open field, or in some other "natural" outdoor setting. And then you die. And you decompose. And the guide of the meditation takes you through the whole thing: your skin blackening, bloating, gasses releasing, decay, until you're nothing but a pile of bones, and then, even less than that: just dust. The focus is on change: how the body doesn't disappear, but changes into other things, and in doing so, feeds all sorts of other things.

That's fine. But what about *me?* And this was a big moment for me: realizing that I don't consider myself to be my body. "I" am something completely different, "I" live *in* my body, and if that's so, then what happens to *me,* or that is to say, my consciousness?

I was thinking about this a lot when I encountered Laurie Anderson's excellent film *The Heart of a Dog.* I was so stunned by this film that I watched it twice, back-to-back. In the film, Anderson's beloved dog Lola dies and she imagines Lola working her way, alone, through the Bardo, the liminal plane of existence that Buddhists like Anderson believe the soul moves through between this life and the next.

When I watched this, a lightbulb turned on in my consciousness: it's that simple. We get to believe whatever we want about what comes next, but the powerful idea for me was this notion of *believing*. Of having faith in an idea.

For me, *non-being* is just too much. I really dislike the notion.

I choose to believe in something else: that we move on from this life and into the next. That if something does happen and my body stops working—I guess I should say *when* that happens—I will be alright, even if my body isn't. I'll just move on to the next thing.

This isn't really a free pass: in fact, in some ways, it is worse. Even if we move on to the next life, we apparently forget all about this one (except in the well-documented cases of young children who remember their past lives), and isn't that horribly sad? We still have to let go of every person and every thing we love in this life: we can't take it with us.

Death is still pretty *meh* in my opinion.

But this idea helps me with the overwhelming, panic-inducing aspect of dying, and so I've embraced it.

And it helps.

Acknowledgements

First and foremost, I want to thank Amanda Ichihashi Jagerman, LCSW, for being my first reader, one of my oldest friends, and for offering valuable insights and commentary from her perspective as a therapist.

Secondly, many thanks to Dr. John Hampsey, whose lectures on Existentialism and Romanticism not only contributed to this book, but also to my own well-being in so many ways.

I also want to thank the therapists in my life, with gratitude towards Dr. Henry Ahlström and Maureen Stegner, who helped me through some of my most difficult spots.

Last, I want to thank my husband, John. Thanks, Bun, for being there for me.

LAY OUT YOUR UNREST